THE JEWS
OF POLAND
IN TALE AND LEGEND

To all dreamers
and story–lovers…

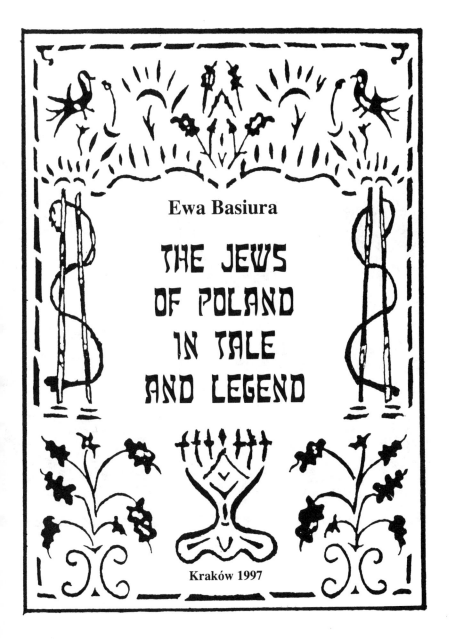

Ewa Basiura

THE JEWS OF POLAND IN TALE AND LEGEND

Kraków 1997

ת׳צחק

Written by
Ewa Basiura

Cover design
Ewa Basiura

Text revision
dr Teresa Bałuk-Ulewicz

© Copyright by STORYTELLER 1997

ISBN 978-83-907702-1-5

Dystrybucja / Distribution: STORYTELLER
+ 48 12 422-86-11

CONTENTS

AUTHOR'S FOREWORD

This book has come into being as a result of my long-lasting interest in Jewish culture and several years of work and research. Its goal is gathering and presenting, in an easily accessible form, the legends and tales about the Jews who came to settle in the territories of Poland, as well as those connected with the well-known figures and places prominent in the Jewish communities in Poland.

There is more to it, however, than just showing this fairy-tale-like contribution to the historical facts. The most essential aspect is, above all, the atmosphere of the world into which, I hope, the stories included in this volume will introduce Readers, both young and adult. History mingles in them with folklore, magic, a belief in demons, supernatural phenomena and the miraculous powers of wonder-rabbis. The history and folk tradition of the Jewish and Polish nations are frequently interwoven, creating a common indivisible plot and testifying to the mutual interrelations of the two cultures. The piling up of these elements for centuries makes it virtually impossible to tell them apart on the level of the story. In the eyes of the Jungian psychoanalysis their interconnections, going back to the distant past and reflected in folklore, belong to the sphere of the collective unconscious. They are stronger than all the divisions and animosities appearing in the everyday reality, even throughout the centuries.

I collected and ordered the "threads" for these stories mostly from oral tradition, and sometimes even from the tales heard from casual acquaintances. Very frequently these were just bits and scraps of stories, fragments of a lost mozaic, out of which it was often very difficult to put together a uniform whole. Some of them I was later able to identify in the academic literature on the subject. This not only confirmed their authenticity, but also became a helpful guideline and criterion for the selection of the material. It also happened that the same events or deeds were connected or attributed to different persons. I then had to make a decision which of them was to become the protagonist of my version of the story. In such cases my choice was in favour of the more famous one.

Another difficulty, which was also a challenge, was the proper choice of the form and the weighing of the style. On one hand I wanted the original motifs not to lose their unique character; on the other I did not want the plot to be reduced to a couple of sentences and the protagonists to be portrayed only by their actions and attitudes. Therefore several times I allowed my imagination to become involved in the elaboration of descriptions, building up the atmosphere and "penetrating" into the thoughts and feelings of the protagonists. This literary "empathy" became an expedient kind of material extremely helpful for filling in the gaps in the stories which I encountered frequently.

In connection with the above, the Reader will not find in this collection the typical examples of Chasidic tales and legends full of mysticism, originating, for instance, from the circles of Baal Shem Tov or Nachman of Braclav. That's because these stories constitute a "literary enclave" and belong to an entirely different world — a person from outside does not possess the necessary insight and the storytelling power to handle them.

I hold the view that to allow a folk tale to make its appeal directly to the human imagination one should not in any way interpret or explain it; therefore I have refrained from any analysis or footnotes. Only nine short introductory notes have some historical and biographical information concerning the people, events or phenomena to which the legends refer.

And now, it is my pleasure to invite the Reader into the enchanted circle of Jewish tales and legends.

E. B.

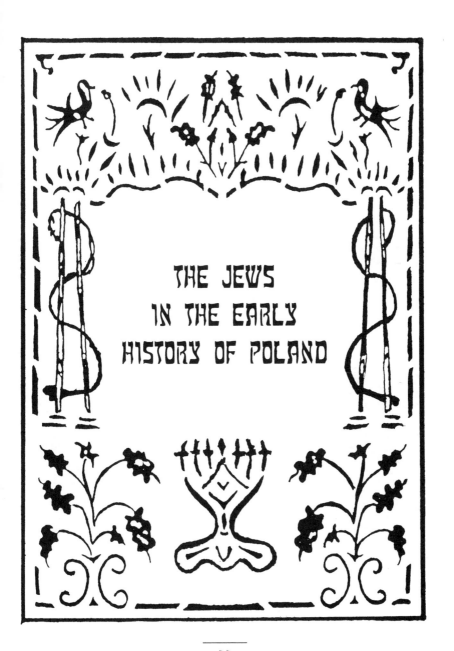

THE JEWS IN THE EARLY HISTORY OF POLAND

he beginnings of the Jewish presence in Poland go back to the last four centuries of the first millennium CE. These were times before the Polish state was formed, and therefore no written records and testimonies are available. It is known, however, that the important commercial routes, which then crossed the area of the present Poland, were used by numerous Jewish merchants, whose contribution towards the development of international trade was notable. Travelling from West to East, they carried mainly textiles and furs and on their way back exotic spices and handicraft goods.

The first written testimonies concerning Poland were made by one such Jewish merchant, Ibrahim ibn Jacob of Spain. The Califf of Cordoba had sent him as an envoy to the Emperor of Germany, Otton the Great. During that diplomatic mission (960-965) he also visited the Slavonic lands and in his account he mentioned, among others, Prince Mieszko, his warriors and Cracow.

It seems possible that already as early as the beginning of the Middle Ages some Jews lived in Poland, but their mass settlement took place simultaneously with the final period of the Crusades. At that time a number of European countries started imposing various limitations and restrictions on Jewish trade and craft, and some cities banned Jewish settlement altogether, on the basis of acts de non tolerandis Judaeis. *An even greater increase in persecution was observed in the second half of the 14th century, under the influence of the Inquisition, which culminated in the expulsion of the Jews from Spain and Portugal in 1492.*

For many centuries Jewish people would find shelter in Poland, which in time became one of the largest centres of Jewish religious and cultural life in the world. The Polish princes and kings of the House of Piast, especially Prince Boleslaus the Pious and King Casimir the Great, lavished special care and privileges on the Jews. Already in this distant past Jewish communities enjoyed organizational autonomy and had their own jurisdiction in Poland.

HOW ABRAHAM THE MERCHANT ALMOST BECAME A POLISH PRINCE

Once upon a time, in Kruszwica, a settlement upon Gopło Lake, there ruled Prince Popiel, whose cruelty was such that his subjects trembled at the very mention of his name. Eventually, however, though not soon, his good fortune did change and justice was done. After many years of his wicked and tyrannical reign fate led him to meet his frightful end. One dark night thousands of mice emerged from the local woods and invaded Popiel's castle. In no time the Prince, his wife as well as his corrupted servants lost their lives, devoured by the vermin.

Once the news of this spread in the area, the Council of Elders assembled in Kruszwica and began heated disputes who should become the new Prince of Poland. The deliberations continued for many a day and night, no one, however, seemed to be worthy of the honour. One was too old to be the ruler, another too young, still another had a reputation for a quick temper. Thus the Elders became despondent and sorrowful, till on the seventh day, at dawn, a brilliant idea occurred to one of them. Since all the councils and debates had proved futile and the Assembly had failed to elect a Prince from among themselves, why shouldn't they rely on Fate's decree? The idea this man had put forward appealed to everyone. It was therefore decided that on that day, the first newcomer, save a woman, who stepped onto the bridge leading to Kruszwica would be acclaimed Prince of Poland.

Once it had been agreed the Elders left the table and forming a solemn procession, walked together towards the city gate. The dwellers of Kruszwica accompanied them numerously, as everyone

Prince Piast

wanted to witness the moment when a stranger would accede to such an honourable position. Hardly had the crowd reached the bridge when a group of people approaching the city appeared on the horizon. Everyone anxiously awaited the grand moment which seemed so close at hand. Nearer and nearer came the wayfarers, and their silhouettes could already be distinctly seen. Doubtless they were foreign merchants, for the wagons, as well as the horses they led were loaded with an immense store of goods. The people viewed the strangers with visible curiousity and amazement. They were clad in long, outlandish garments and their hats were also of foreign form. However, what caught the eye most were their bushy, long and curly beards. Ahead of the group, carved stick in hand, walked a man of noble countenance, no longer a youth but still in the prime of his life. His clothes appeared to be richer than those of his fellows, and his face, darkened by wind and sun, denoted a man of distinction and wisdom.

As soon as he had put his first step on Kruszwica Bridge one of the Elders, called Slavomysl, stepped out of the crowd. He was the oldest among the members of the Council, so his was the privilege to greet the merchant and break to him the news about the vacant prince's throne awaiting him. The two men met in the middle of the bridge and conversed for awhile. No one, however, could hear the words, as there was a considerable distance between them and the throng. Soon enough the merchant motioned his companions, who stood near the bridge, to follow him to the city. He and Slavomysl led the way through the gate. The Elder explained to the curious crowd that the newcomer was a Jewish merchant from a distant land and that Abraham was his name. He did not consent at once to accept the honour bestowed upon him, but asked for three days' time to ponder over the matter. As he had said, it was God, not man, who was to decide on such significant issues.

17

Thus Abraham and the remaining merchants were led to a large, richly furnished house, in the very centre of the city. There, for three days and just as many nights, they were to offer up prayers to their God, so that He should help Abraham to reach the right decision. On entering the princely dwelling the Jews closed the door behind themselves, drew the curtains in the windows and went into prayer and meditation, which they continued without accepting any food.

When the appointed time had come the inhabitants of Kruszwica, together with their Elders gathered around the house. Long did they wait for the door to open, but the house remained as still as if there were not a living soul inside. No one dared to interfere with the visitors' prayers and it could not be predicted how much longer the waiting would take. Suddenly, however, an energetic and vigorous man left the crowd. Before anyone could stop him he had thrusted himself forward and started banging on the door with both his fists.

In an instant everyone became silent with awe and looked in fear at the rascal, in whom they recognized Piast the Wheeler. The man kept knocking till finally the door opened and Abraham appeared in it. His face was radiant with some unearthly light. Everbody was filled with certainty that the God to whom the merchant had been praying was truly a mighty God. Abraham spoke out. He explained he could not accept the honour conferred upon him, but he was ordained to point to the man who deserved it and would reign over the Poles justly and wisely. Having said this he stretched out his hand towards Piast. If that man had had so much courage not to hesitate to disturb them while they were praying, then obviously God had willed that to happen. The wise counsel was willingly accepted and in this way Piast the Wheeler came to be the Prince of Poland. Abraham and his fellow-merchants settled down in Kruszwica and lived there peacefully, practising various crafts, trading with the local people, praising their Jewish God and always giving people good advice.

HOW THE SAINTLY RABBIS SAVED THE COUNTRY FROM DROUGHT

Were we to browse through the old chronicles we would not learn about these events, as all-consuming time, and often also fire have devoured the oldest parchments. Only in the memory of the people have these tales been preserved and passed from one generation onto another. Sometimes children may hear them from various wanderers, beggars and travelling merchants. From time to time someone makes a song about them and hums it in the household or in the field...

In those distant days the Polish lands enjoyed lasting peace and the country was rich and fertile. It was bathed in milk and honey as the writings say. The people ploughed the fields and lived in happiness and harmony, under the wise and just rule of the Princes of the House of Piast. Foreign merchants coming here from near and afar could safely and without any fear traverse the roads and fields. In the neighbouring countries meanwhile, new conflicts would, now and again, arise and often bloody wars broke out as well. People suffered immensely there and more than one man had to seek shelter in foreign lands. Many of them arrived in the country of the Polish people, as the news had widely spread that a warm welcome and sincere hospitality was always to be expected there.

In the times when Prince Leszek was the ruler of Poland a grave disaster befell the Jewry of Germany, who suffered dreary persecution. They not only lacked the strength to defend themselves and to fight weapon in hand, but they also wanted to avoid bloodshed, which was against the principles of their faith. Soon they realised the time had come for them to leave and settle elsewhere. The decision was taken to send some sages as envoys to the Polish court to implore protection of the Prince. As it had been planned, so it was done.

Seven distinguished rabbis, whose heads and beards had been touched with the silver of old age, started out on the journey. For many a day they travelled, hardly taking time to sleep, and if they ever stopped it was only for a light meal and a prayer, in which they begged the Almighty to bless their mission. They had traversed thick and dark forests, which seemed to be endless, till one day in the morning dense trees and bushes thinned out. The weary travellers were encouraged by the sight of the vast and golden fields of Poland. Now the goal of their journey was no longer so distant. One more day they travelled in the scorching summer heat till finally the sunset saw them reach the gates of the Prince's castle.

Not before long were they led to Prince Leszek, who was feasting in a huge, wooden hall in the company of his eminent warriors. The rabbis explained the nature of their mission at length. Not only did they tell the Prince about the misfortunes that had befallen the Jewish nation and the sufferings this had caused, but also about the might of the Jewish God, Jehovah. Having heard the plea Leszek decided to let the Jews settle in his land, upon which the grateful rabbis offered to do him a favour. The ruler opened his heart to his foreign guests, telling them about his great worry. He said that for many, many days not even a single raindrop had fallen on the fields of Poland. Should the drought last a week longer, the crops in the entire country would be ruined. The saintly rabbis promised to pray to God to bless the hospitable land with rain. In the chamber given to them by the Prince the old sages kept vigil all night long, chanting prayers with so much passion that they must have soared to God's throne in the highest heaven.

On the following day, in the morning, when the Prince woke up and looked out of the window his heart was filled with joy at the sight of a dark sky overcast with heavy, lead-coloured clouds. Presently a downpour came and watered the thirsty fields. Leszek rejoiced at that sure sign of Heaven's grace and knew he had been right in fulfilling the rabbis' request and allowing the Jewish people to come and live in Poland.

HOW THE JEWS OF SPAIN CAME TO POLAND

More than five centuries have passed since the time when a wave of atrocious persecution of the Jewish people swept through the kingdoms of Spain and Portugal. Before those times they had lived a comfortable and affluent life in both these countries. Once the misfortune struck the Jews, however, the hopes for the future were no longer bright and there were only two ways to choose between. They could either abandon their dwellings and try to seek a better life in other parts of the world or convert to Christianity. The decision was not an easy one. Those who accepted the new religion, but practised their old faith secretly, were liable to severe punishment. Thus for the majority exile and the fate of eternal wanderers seemed to be the only acceptable way out and they humbly resigned themselves into it.

The Jews directed their steps in different directions. Some of them went to the south, the others headed eastwards. It was a sorry peregrination, whose destination was obscured by the haze of the unknown. Somewhere far away, under the sunny Spanish skies, the mossgrown graves of the forefathers had to be left behind.

The exiled people travelled in large groups so that they could protect themselves against brigands and highwaymen lurking in the woods. Sometimes several families or even a whole community would walk together with their pious rabbi. The further eastward they went, the more they suffered from the cold, and the nature around them grew wilder and wilder. The forests became thicker and more shadowy and the sough of the trees was so strange that it almost sounded hostile. The parties of Jewish wanderers were led by elderly, long-bearded men, the family patriarchs who walked with the aid of staves or were sometimes supported by younger and stronger men. The children would usually cling to their mothers, who carried the youngest ones in their arms. All the possessions of those people seemed to consist of the holy scrolls carried with due care and reverence by the youths.

After many months of such pilgrimage, which seemed to take as long as the forefathers' way through the desert, some of the wayfarers reached a brighter place in the forest where the trees were fewer and sun-beams played among the leaves like forerunners of hope. Eventually they came upon a green, grassy clearing. A light breeze played with the leaves of grass, which were as delicate as the softest carpet and appeared to be inviting the weary travellers to take a rest. They were standing motionless, admiring the sight and it was then that a heavenly voice became audible over their heads. The exiles heard it say: Poh-lin! The words were uttered in the sacred Hebrew tongue and they meant: "here is your rest. " Thus the Jews settled in the land revealed to them by God's voice and since that time they have called it Polin, which means Poland.

THE WORLD
OF DEMONS

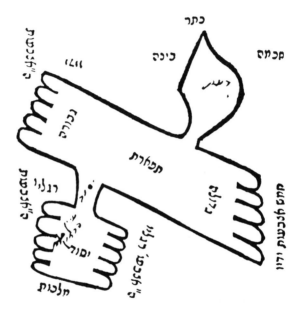

he Jewish belief in numerous demons, dibbuks and other super-natural beings goes back to the period of Jewish history follow-ing the Babylonian captivity and it contains many elements which can also be found in Persian mythology. A real treasure trove of tales about spirits and demons is, however, the Aggadic section of the Talmud. In the 18th century, the "evolution" of the supernatural imagery was largely aided by the Chasidim, who delighted in spin-ning unusual stories of wonders, magic and of the world of the hostile spirits, whose main aim was to lead human souls astray.

Practically until the time when the Second World War annihilat-ed the Jewish shtetl of Eastern Europe, which had been a treasury of old belief and custom, for the average Jew the everyday, material reality intermingled with the ominous world of the invisible beings. Their legions, ruled by Satan and his mistress Lilith, lurked in all sorts of gloomy places like old, uninhabited houses, dark cellars, ruins, hollow trees, forests and wetlands. With the onset of darkness their power always grew bigger. That is why people avoided walking or travelling alone at night. On an everyday basis many rules of behaviour were observed by way of protection and numerous charms and herbs were also used for this purpose. As these deterrents, how-ever, sometimes proved ineffective, the fear of the dark forces could be removed completely and cast away only on the Sabbath, when the evil spirits were deprived of their destructive powers.

Demons would possess mostly sinners, as access to them was the easiest. Men were most often seduced by Lilith, who assumed the shape of a beautiful, passionate woman. Children born of such unions were half-demons and half-humans. Very frequently places haunted by such infernal forces could only be freed of them by means of exor-cisms performed by the most eminent and saintly rabbis.

Apotropaic stones

A HAUNTED HOUSE IN POSEN AND A RABBINIC TRIAL OF DEMONS

These events took place at the end of the 17th century in Posen, in one of the town houses belonging to the Jewish community and situated in the Market Square. From time immemorial the door to its cellar had been locked with seven bolts and seven seals. The owners of the house had often changed, but somehow everyone knew that the cellar should not be entered, as some terrible and gloomy mystery from the distant past was connected with the place. Human curiousity, however, is invincible and much stronger than fear, especially when combined with young age and lack of experience. Thus, one day, a reckless adventurer turned up and decided to investigate the matter.

The youth went to the cellar down the spiral stairs with a candle in one hand, and a box full of tools and various keys in the other. Hardly had he started to tinker with the rusty locks, when a high-pitched scream and sinister laughter could be heard. A sudden gust of cold wind coming out of nowhere put out the boy's candle. Unearthly voices reverberated throughout the neighbourhood. They attracted a number of people, who despite their fear hurried downstairs to see what had happened to the careless youngster. They were petrified to find him lying dead, his body terribly mutilated, in front of the still closed cellar door.

After that event the inhabitants of the house did not have a single minute of peace. The Evil which had so far resided in the dark depths of the cellar abandoned its hellish dwellings and started haunting their apartments. Invisible forces would knock candlestics and cups off the shelves, break dishes and pollute the Sabbath food by putting ash and other impurities into it. The local rabbis tried hard to drive the demons away by means of diverse amulets, charms and incantations, but to no avail. Finally an idea occurred to someone that they should contact a famous miracle-worker, Rabbi Joel Baal Shem of Zamoshtsh, and request his help. Messengers were promptly appointed by the community and sent to the celebrated sage, well-read in magic and the Kabbalah. Having listened affably to their plea he consented to come to Posen.

Once the saintly man came to the city he gathered a group of the local rabbis and in this pious company he crossed the threshold of the notorious house. He immediately commenced the incantations, invoking the holy names in the hope of overcoming the forces of evil. After the demons had made themselves heard Rabbi Joel bade them explain how they had taken possession of the place. He was answered that the house belonged to them forever by the right of heredity and the infernal spirits were so sure of themselves that they agreed to argue their case before a jury. Soon a trial was held in a make-shift court-room, furnished in the house for this purpose. One demon turned up as a representative of the defendants. No one could see him, however, and even the saintly rabbis were only able to hear his voice.

The impure spirit started telling a story of a certain wealthy gold-smith who had dwelt in the house with his family many years before and had a workshop in the cellar. Once he happened to be on a journey at night-time and demonic voices led him astray. Under the threat of quartering him alive they made him marry one of Lilith's daughters. On that very day his workshop in the cellar had been miraculously trans-formed into an underground chamber into which the she-devil came to live. The goldsmith visited the place every night and fathered three sons on her. Their nature was therefore half-human and half-demonic.

Once, at Passover, during the Seder, he was suddenly overcome with the feeling of burning lust and longing for his hellborn mistress. Under some trifle pretence he left the table and went down to the cellar. Worried by his long absence, his wife followed him to the workshop. She found the door closed, but she could distinctly hear voices coming from behind it, so she peeped in through the keyhole. The sight revealed to her eyes was truly amazing. Instead of a cramped and shabby cellar room she saw a magnificent chamber gorgeously adorned with gold. In the middle of it stood a huge bed, in which, embraced by a nude woman, lay her husband. Not for a second did the wife doubt that what she had seen was the doing of evil forces. Without delay she ran to the rabbi and told him all about it.

As soon as the holiday season was over the rabbi summoned the goldsmith and questioned him about the whole thing. The unfortunate man tried various explanations and excuses but the pious rabbi did not let himself be deceived. Since lying was no good the goldsmith confessed the whole truth, which the rabbi had long guessed anyway. He gave the culprit a charm which had a protective power against demons. The goldsmith rejoiced, yet the worry about his demonic offspring clouded his happiness. After having discussed the problem the two men found a seemingly plausible solution. The cellar was to be given to his demon sons for a lodging, but with seven bolts and as many seals put on the door, lest no man be in danger of evil possession. The instructions had been carried out to the minutest detail and so many generations of people had lived in the house undisturbed that the memory of the goldsmith and his story had gradually fallen into oblivion. Once, however, this reckless fellow tried to break the door the infernal forces were set free and sneaked into human quarters.

Hearing the demon's arguments, Rabbi Joel Baal Shem fell into thought. In his great wisdom he soon found a way to approach the problem and was ready to pass a just judgement. He declared that only the cellar had been given to the demons and they had had no right to enter the apartments. Having violated this prohibition they themselves had jeopardized their right to the cellar and were now ordered to quit the place. The Rabbi concluded the pronouncement of his verdict by invoking the holy names and chanting kabbalistic formulas, thus ordering the evil forces to abandon the place forever.

As soon as the Rabbi had uttered his last word the air became alive with the flutter of myriads of invisible wings, as well as with various humming and hissing noises. Whole legions of demons were leaving the house through the chimney and the windows. All these spirits, who had multiplied in the cellar for years, were descendants of the said goldsmith. The infernal squeals and the racket made the foundations of the house shake and the time the demons took to fly away seemed endless. Finally all was silence. The golden palace chamber turned again into a dark cellar, but since that time the tenants of the house have never been bothered by any supernatural manifestations.

THE REMUH CEMETERY

The Remuh Cemetery

One of the oldest Jewish cemeteries in Poland is situated in Cracow's district of Kuzmir. It is enclosed in the quadrangle of four streets, Szeroka, Miodowa, Jakuba and Ciemna. Established in 1552, for almost 250 years, till 1800, it served as a burial ground for many a generation of the local Jews. During the subsequent centuries, when a new cemetery was already in use, eminent people were still interred in the old one.

The cemetery, together with the adjoining synagogue, constitutes a unique place of worship, as well as a monument of the history and culture of the Jewish nation, visited today by thousands of Jews from all over the world. The grave of Rabbi Moses Isserles, also known as Remuh (1525-1572), is a particularly venerated spot. He made a name for himself in the Diaspora for being a distinguished Talmud scholar and a great authority on questions of ritual. He opened his own Yeshivah in Cracow, but it was his work, "Mappa, " adjusting the "Shulkhan Arukh" to the needs of the Ashkhenazi Jews, that brought him worldwide fame.

The grave of the Rabbi is situated in the part of the cemetery along the western wall of the synagogue. Its tombstone was one of the few which were not devastated during the Second World War. Many people consider this fact to be a miracle. Those who come to pray here frequently put notes into the box situated near the Rabbi's grave, asking Moses Isserles to intercede for them before God.

The legend about the old Jewish cemetery in Cracow, included in this collection, has unfortunately nothing to do with the historical facts, as it obviously speaks of the period before the establishment of the Remuh Cemetery. The bubonic plague mentioned in it can be identified, with a considerable dose of probability, as the one ravaging Europe in the middle of the 14th century. At this time the Jewish quarter was situated in the area of today's Ulica Świętej Anny. The cemetery, of which no visible trace has remained, must have been located outside the defensive walls of the city. The Jews moved to Kuzmir much later, at the beginning of the 16th century.

Despite such disregard of historical facts the value of the legend cannot be denied, as it constitutes an interesting testimony of the

Jewish presence in Cracow, thus bridging the gap of time and space between two old cemeteries: the one which is no more and the other which has been preserved till today. That is why it is worth pondering over during a visit to Cracow's district of Kuzmir and Rabbi Remuh's grave.

A WEDDING IN THE OLD JEWISH CEMETERY IN CRACOW

Six centuries ago, and maybe more, in times beyond the reach of memory, a wave of bubonic plague, which swept through Europe, mercilessly claimed its numerous victims. Neither did it spare the royal city of Cracow. The plague took its ghastly toll and there was no day without hundreds of deaths. Old people, youths, women and innocent infants alike died in terrible pain. The streets of the city were almost empty, as those who remained alive locked themselves up in their homes, making sure there was not a single crack or crevice in the doors and windows. By doing so they all hoped to escape the claws of death. Yet all these efforts turned out to be vain and the Angel of Death entered the houses one after another. Every morning from behind the closed window shutters loud lamentations could be heard, as so many people mourned their relatives.

In the synagogues of the Jewish quarter prayers were raised to God imploring Him to avert the holy anger from His people. It even happened that, out of fear, the rich, who had always been indifferent to human misery, started giving generously to the poor. Still, neither the prayers nor virtuous deeds were powerful enough to stop the plague which ravaged the city like a fury at large.

And then suddenly someone remembered an old custom, supposed to appease the plague, practised sometimes in the little towns and villages. The community would arrange, at its own expense, a wedding of two cripples in the Jewish cemetery. This idea was taken up by the Jews of Cracow, who clung to it as if this were their last bit of hope. The

Kahal Council allotted for this purpose an appropriate amount of money from its funds. The preparations for the ceremony were carried out scrupulously. However, when everything was almost ready, a problem suddenly emerged. While the people were busy making the food and putting up the chuppah it skipped everyone's mind to look for the prospective couple who would take their place under the wedding canopy. Thus a mad search started. The men soon found a proper groom in the poorhouse and brought him to the cemetery. It was Feivel, a hunchback blind in one eye. The women brought him a bride, the lame Rifke, who having no home of her own earned her living by performing menial tasks at people's households in return for a bit of food and a place to sleep.

Thus, on a late Friday afternoon the two faced each other and were wed under the chuppah. Feivel slipped a tin wedding ring onto Rifke's finger, smashed a cup with his foot and the crowd of guests heartily shouted "Mazel tov! " Dancing began and the party was soon in full swing. Among the revelry and joy, accompanied by music and laughter, all the worries seemed to pale and become distant. No one thought of the plague any more. The wedding guests did not even take any heed of the fact that the dusk had made the sky grow dark and that the sun had long set, making room for the moon and the stars and announcing the advent of the Sabbath. Not to welcome the holiday properly was a grave sin against God's commandment, for which the joyful and merry revellers were duly punished.

From under their whirling, dancebound feet the earth seemed to be escaping quicker and quicker. Dancing ceased suddenly and the music stopped in midbar. Everyone stood petrified as if turned into stone, resembling the gloomy tombstones around them. Only then did they notice that the earth was trembling violently. Each subsequent quake grew stronger and more menacing till suddenly the crust of the earth tore open, showing a fiery abyss, like a voracious mouth of a hellish beast. In no more than one second it swallowed up the dancers and the earth shut up as suddenly as it had opened. The heavy silence of death enveloped the cemetery and the entire Jewish quarter. Only the preternatural silence of the days of Genesis could have been so terrible, before the first blaze of light kissed the earth and let it be filled with life...

It is said that since then it has been forbidden to hold weddings on Fridays and that there were no more funerals in the old cemetery. Its gate was walled up and remained like this to the beginning of a terrible war...

The "Wailing Wall" in the Remuh Cemetery

EISIK'S SYNAGOGUE

Eisik's Synagogue

At the corner of Ulica Izaaka and Ulica Jakuba (No 25), towering above the neighbourhood, there stands a mighty, Baroque edifice called Eisik's Synagogue, named so after its founder, Isaac Jacobovitsh son of Jacob Eberles. The legend describes him as a pauper who came to wealth after having found a treasure hidden in his garden. In reality he was a descendant of one of the richest merchant families in Poland at that time. He himself was the wealthiest Jewish merchant, banker and owner of numerous houses and stalls in the 17th-century Cracow. Respected by the whole community, Reb Eisik performed the duties of the Kahal's Senior for many years.

The erection of the Synagogue founded by him was started in 1638, after King Vladislaus IV's permission had been obtained. It lasted till 1644, the year in which the court proceedings in connection with the matter were concluded. They had been started under the influence of the parish priest of the nearby Church of Corpus Christi, who had opposed the building of a synagogue so close to his church.

Impressive in size, but simple in form, the building had a beautiful, richly furnished Baroque interior. It is believed to have been the object of an attack of the local rowdies, attracted by the hope of rich loot. They did not succeed in their plans, however, because the Kuzmir Jews had been forewarned in time, and played a trick on them. Clad in white funerary shrouds, they hid in the Remuh Cemetery in wait for the robbers. The pallid figures emerging suddenly from the cemetery amid the darkness of night must have been a ghastly sight indeed, as the thieves took to their heels, raising clouds of dust after themselves.

During the Second World War the Synagogue was plundered and fell into ruin. Several years after the War it was restored and was used by the Union of Artists. However, in the eighties the full-scale restoration works began to bring the Synagogue to its former splendour.

Eisik's Synagogue

REB EISIK'S DREAM

Over three hundred years ago, in Kuzmir, a Jewish quarter in Cracow, there lived a pious Jew called Eisik. Although in his earnest prayers he praised God day and night it happened to him more than once to know the taste of poverty. Despite this misery, he never gave up his faith and accepted his plight like Job, humbly and without rebellion. He did not even ask God to change his sorry fate. Such incredible humility soon came to be noticed in the Heavenly Spheres and was also duly rewarded.

One night, when Reb Eisik was sleeping soundly, he saw in his dream an exceptionally beautiful city with golden roofs, and in it a mighty, stone brigde across a foamy, swift-flowing river. Somewhere, behind this vision, he heard a mysterious voice commanding him to go to this Bohemian city, called Prague, without delay. There, on the bridge across the Veltava River, Eisik would hear some good news, which was to change all his life. He woke up in the morning with a vivid memory of the dream and could not help pondering over it all day long. To a poor man like him, however, it seemed too difficult a task to leave his wife and little children and venture on such a long journey on foot. Yet, when the dream recurred for two more nights, and when the voice seemed to sound angry, Reb Eisik decided not to linger any further.

On the third day he took a walking stick and a traveller's bundle, bid his family farewell and directed his steps towards the city of his revelation. After long and exhausting wanderings, which took months on end, the weary traveller entered the city which looked exactly like the one in his dream. Soon he found the river and the same stone bridge, which he approached with his heart throbbing madly. He walked slowly, glancing at the rapid waters of the Veltava River and admiring the Hradcany Castle situated on a hill, towering over the city. He kept strolling along the bridge to and fro, expecting to hear the promised good tidings, but no such thing happened.

Eisik was trying hard to free himself of the thought that the dream had just been a meaningless vision. He trusted in God's power with all his might and came to the bridge day after day to continue his walking vigilance till, on the seventh day, a stranger came up to him. The man, who judging by his dress was a Gentile, asked about Eisik's reason for spending so much time on the bridge, as whenever he passed it he could see the lonely figure of the Jew whose sorrowful eyes seemed to be looking for something or someone in the crowd. Eisik confided in the stranger, telling him about the dream he had had. However, some inexplicable force from within him kept Eisik from revealing his name as well as the place where he came from.

After having listened to the story the Gentile burst into a fit of laughter. So naive did Reb Eisik seem to him with his faith in phantoms. When he composed himself he told the Jew the story of his own dream of similar nature. A mysterious voice had informed him of some priceless treasure buried among the roots of an old pear-tree in Cracow, in the garden of a Jew called Eisik. Nevertheless it did not even enter the man's head to believe in these reveries and undertake such a distant journey to Poland.

After the stranger had said goodbye and taken his leave, still laughing and shaking his head in disbelief, Reb Eisik thanked God on the highest, and at a lively pace made his way back to Cracow. This time the journey seemed less strenuous and much shorter, as the good news gave Eisik a lot of strength. Immediately on his return home he took to digging in the garden, under the old tree. Hardly had he made a few movements with his spade when the tool hit a huge metal coffer. He lifted its heavy lid and found a treasure of treasures inside. It consisted of so much gold and so many precious jewels that it made the former pauper one of the richest men in Cracow's Kuzmir.

May no one, however, think that Reb Eisik used that wealth just for himself and his family. He shared many a gem with the poor and as he felt obliged to thank God for that happy turn of fortune, he had a magnificent synagogue erected. It was named after its founder and today may still be viewed in Kuzmir.

A figure of a Jew

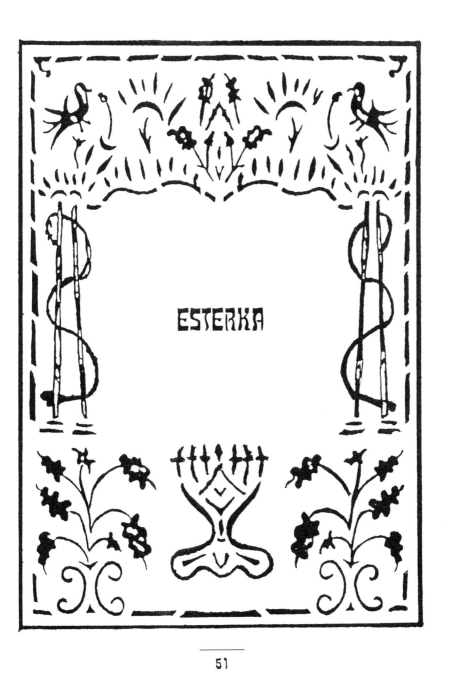

ESTERKA

Esterka, the mistress of King Casimir the Great in the last years of his life, is a bizarre figure. Neither the dates of her birth and death nor any facts from her biography are known. It cannot even be said with certainty that she really existed. Nevertheless she not only appears in legends and folk tales, but also as a vivid Romantic heroine in the Polish 19th century literature. She is often presented as an influential protectress of the Jewish people, sharing some features with the Biblical Esther. One of the best known novels which tells her story is "Król chłopów" (1881; The Peasant King) by Ignacy Kraszewski. She also appears in Yiddish literature, among others in Aaron Zeitlin's drama entitled Esterke (1932).

Tradition connects her name with many towns and villages in Poland, among others with Łobzów, Opoczno, Kazimierz Dolny (Kuzmir) or Bochotnica. In some of them manor-houses are shown which are said to have been given by the King to his beloved mistress. The park in Łobzów is also mentioned as her burial place.

The first record concerning Esterka can be found in the "History of Poland" by Jan Długosz (15th century), which was written more than one hundred years after King Casimir's death. The chronicler describes her as a woman of rare beauty, with which she bewitched the monarch. He was supposed to have fathered two sons on her. Their names were Niemierza and Pełka. Two daughters who were also born of this union were, with the King's consent, brought up in the Jewish religion.

The influential relationship of the King with Esterka was allegedly the reason for the numerous privileges and freedoms granted to the Polish Jews during Casimir's reign. Długosz's history, however, does not seem to be a reliable document and source of information. In the footnote to its 1984 edition we read that the mother of the two sons mentioned was in fact Cudka, wife of Niemierza of Gołczyn.

KING CASIMIR THE GREAT AND ESTERKA

K ing Casimir, who was rightly nicknamed the Great, loved dearly the common folk and simple people. The Monarch enjoyed their company so much that lest they be not overawed by the greatness of his majesty he would frequently put on garments of a wanderer and roam the Polish villages and towns in this disguise. He always wanted to know if the people lived happy lives and were not troubled by any want.

Once, on one of these errands, he arrived in the evening at a tiny settlement. The night was about to flood the whole world with darkness, so the King decided to seek the hospitality of his subjects. Thus he came up to the nearest cottage and knocked at the door, since its brightly illuminated windows seemed to be inviting him to make a stop there. And the King was not mistaken, as the door opened promptly for him and he was led into a large room. However, his amazement was great when he saw the family of the house. Both their dress and speech testified to the fact that the King had not found himself in a peasant's household.

He cast a curious look around and soon realized that the good people who had offered their hospitality to him were of the Jewish religion and that he was obviously in the midst of some festive celebrations. He was seated at a richly set table, to which the host had invited him, and was asked to partake of the meal. While eating and savouring the taste of the pancakes thickly sprinkled with fragrant cinnamon, the King, being completely unfamiliar with the Jewish customs, paid attention to everything that was going on around him. At one moment he happened to galnce into a distant corner of the room. Near the window there he noticed a small lamp, finely wrought in silver. Eight bright flames flickered gaily in its tiny vessels, resembling bells or thimbles. Nearby, removed into the shade, sat a young woman with her gaze pensively penetrating the darkness outside. Though she was sitting sideways and the King was unable to see the features of her face distinctly, he could not stop looking at her. As if enchanted he observed her slim, girlish figure, clad in a bright dress embroidered with golden thread, which contrasted with the shock of her long black hair, which flowed softly to the floor in abundant ringlets. Suddenly, as if aware of someone's gaze, the girl turned her head, showing a face of almost unearthly beauty. For a split second her gentle dark eyes met those of the King. The sight of the stranger made her spring up and leave the room hastily.

At that moment the host addressed his guest:

`Please forgive me Sir, that my daughter, Esther, has left us so suddenly. It is because she is rather unaccustomed to the presence of strangers in the house and your glance must have made her feel uneasy.'

It occurred to King Casimir that he could do something good for the girl, so he chose to reveal his identity to Esther's father and offered to take the maiden to his castle in Cracow, where she could become one of the Queen's ladies-in-waiting. The father, however, would not even hear of this, as it was unthinkable for him to let his only daughter live among people of a different religion. For fear of the King's anger, he chose his words carefully while explaining the matter. The royal guest, however, understood the fatherly care and feelings well enough, so he did not insist any more.

After a plentiful supper the King went outside to breathe in some cool evening air. While he was standing there, looking up at the starry winter sky, he heard a delicate woman's voice behind him. He looked back and saw Esther who spoke to him in the following words:

`I did hear your conversation with my father, Sire, and I am ready to go to the court with you, even against his will. I promise to be a most faithful servant of yours. '

The spirited words of the young woman surprised the King immensely, but before he had time to respond she added:

`Tomorrow morning, when you're leaving, I'll be awaiting Your Majesty at the fringe of the nearby woods. '

Having said so Esther hurried back into the house, leaving the King alone with his thoughts amidst the frosty darkness of a winter night.

Next morning King Casimir said goodbye to his host and rewarded his hospitality with a purse of gold. With his heart heavy he started off to meet the fate to which he had silently consented the previous evening. Soon, riding by the woods, he saw the fragile silhouette of Esther, who, true to her word, awaited him there.

How did this story develop? It is not difficult to guess, as it must have been love at first sight that made the girl disobey her father. Since the King reciprocated her feelings, Esther became his mistress. She bore him two sons and two daughters. He loved her so dearly that he had a number of manor-houses built for her in various parts of Poland and as the awareness that he had wronged her father never left the King, he became a protector of all the Jewish people inhabiting his land, conferring many privileges upon them.

ISRAEL
BAAL SHEM TOV

A figure of a Jew

The founder of the Chasidism, Israel Ben Eliezer, known later as Besht (an acrostic of the nickname Baal Shem Tov) was born in 1699 or 1700, most probably in Okop. Orphaned in early childhood he concentrated on his inner and religious experience, leading the life of a hermit and announcing that serving God should be the source of great joy for man.

Already at the age of 30 he became famous as a miracle-worker and healer, however the beginning of his religious activity is connected with the year 1746, when he had a mystic vision. During this experience his soul flew to Heaven and was honoured with seeing the Messiah. During their communion it was revealed to Besht that the Messianic Era would come when his teaching spread all over the world. Since then Baal Shem started his preaching, which was done independently of the kahal organization and often even in opposition to some rabbis. Teaching and talking about God, in a clear everyday language, Besht roamed many villages of Podolia and Volin and crowds of simple, uneducated Jews gathered around him. The Talmud was too difficult for these people to understand and they hungered for simple words. Baal Shem Tov revealed to them that a soul may worship God not only in a synagogue, but also during the everyday household chores provided they were performed with joy and offered up to the Almighty. He gave priority to ardent prayer over the studying of the Torah, as the former had the power to free the sparkles of the divine light trapped in the world of matter. Very frequently this prayer was accompanied by singing, dancing as well as mystic ecstasy.

Besht's amulets and herbs were famous for their miraculous power of healing all kinds of ailments and protecting people from the evil eye. It was believed that if he chose to travel to Jerusalem he would hasten the coming of the Messiah by this act. What's more, Baal Shem had the reputation of a real saint not only among the Jews, but also among the Gentiles.

Besht died in 1760 in Mezhbizh, leaving crowds of his disciples in mourning. Soon afterwards he became a kind of a hero-figure and a vast body of oral and written records, folk tales and legends about him came into being. They gave account of the miraculous healings and the wonders he worked. His teaching, on the other hand, was full of such vital forces that the Chasidic movement initiated by him continued to develop, taking the form of a unique, independent "religion of protest". Its institutionalization, combined with its coming closer to the Orthodox Judaism, became a notable phenomenon only at the end of the 19th century.

BESHT AND HIS MIRACLES

Besht was renowned in the villages of Volin and Podolia for his miraculous healing powers, so many sick people asked him for prayers and interecession before God. He never refused help to anyone and also visited the bedridden in their homes.

It happended once that he restored the health of a man without limbs, after having prayed at his bedside and putting his own hat on the poor man's head.

Another time, in a truly miraculous way, he healed the wife of a wealthy nobleman. The woman, though young and of extreme beauty, had lost all the strength in her hands, which being motionless resembled two dried branches of a barren tree. The husband spared no gold on various potions, medicines and remedies. He contacted all the physicians and healers he had heard of, but the art of medicine proved completely powerless. Each time the unfortunate young couple travelled to a new doctor, they let some hope enter their hearts, only to discover afterwards the bitter taste of sorrow and disappointment. They had been traversing the Polish lands for many years and visiting even the remotest places, till finally a day had come when they decided to accept the cruel decree of fate, give up the futile search and go back home.

Autumn was about to give way to winter and the first frost had just brushed the last leaves on the trees with its silver touch. The carriage of the two travellers ran rapidly along the roads, bumping on the holes, and the coachman flogged the horses with the hope of reaching some inn before dusk. The unhappy husband, immersed in his thoughts, looked absently out of the carriage window. Suddenly the lonely figure of an old, stooping Jew caught his sight. The man was walking slowly along the side of the road. Acting on the spur of the moment the noble-man ordered the coachman to hold back the horses. He wanted to question the white-bearded old man about his destination. Having learnt the Jew was going to Mezhbizh he offered him a ride in the carriage, as there were still several miles to go and the sun had long hidden itself below the horizon. During the journey the nobleman felt an urge to talk and he unbosomed his sorrows to his travel companion.

The old Jew listened to the whole story with genuine sympathy and told him that in Mezhbizh there dwelt a famous miracle-worker, Baal Shem Tov, also known as Besht, and advised the young man to seek help from him. The couple thanked him warmly for the precious advice. As it was already late when they arrived in Mezhbizh they postponed the visit to Besht till the next day and decided to spend the night at an inn. Early in the morning, almost at daybreak, the nobleman went to Besht's house and told him about his plight. Baal Shem listened to his story attentively and advised the man to return to the inn and wait there patiently for what the future would bring. That is what the noble-man did, but a week passed and no improvement in his wife's condition could be noted. He then ventured another visit to the miracle-worker, but much to his chagrin he heard the same command. After another week the lady still could not move her hands and the husband went to Besht for the third time, though he had almost lost all the hope and faith in him. This time, however, his perseverance was rewarded, as Besht asked to be led to the sick woman.

As soon as they came to the inn, Baal Shem explained to the surprised inn-keeper that he intended to stay there for awhile. He made one condition, however, that during this time no one from outside would be allowed to come in, were it even to be the squire himself. Thus after all the doors had been closed Besht sat near the sick woman and devoted all his attention to studying the holy book he had brought with him.

In the meantime, in the nearby manor, the local squire was giving a festive supper to honour his brother who had come on a visit. While they were chatting about this and that, the host casually mentioned the inn he had just had erected in the neighbourhood. His brother, notorious for being a swaggerer, and a drunk into the bargain, sprung up at the news. Although the table groaned with food and drink he insisted on taking an errand to the inn. Eagerly, with a gloat in his eyes, he ran to the stable, saddled a horse, mounted it and galloped in the indicated direction. Hardly had he passed the gate of the manor garden, however, when a most terrible blizzard was unleashed. It had taken the rascal a long time before, blinded by the lashing snow and frozen to the bone, he reached the inn and knocked at its door with his stiffened hand. To his amazement and anger no one hastened to open and the answer came from inside that Besht had given an order not to let anyone in. Fuming with fury, not taking any notice of this warning, the youth kept banging on the door and windows with both his fists.

Inside, the frightened inn-keeper looked askance at Besht, knowing that the situation might put him into serious trouble. Thus Baal Shem allowed him to let the intruder in. The young squire was so maddened with anger that he produced a knife from his pocket and lifted his hand at Besht. At that very moment the healer shouted to the woman: "Put up your hands!" All the people present saw a miracle of miracles performed. The woman, her health restored, lifted her hands at Besht's command, as if she had never been affected by any illness. The people in the inn looked at the utmost happiness of the young couple, but then everyone was distracted by the sound of an object falling to the floor. It was the knife dropped by the squire, whose hands were suddenly touched with paralysis.

In this way, answering Besht's prayer, God restored health to the young noblewoman and punished the wicked squire.

HOW BAAL SHEM GRANTED THREE WISHES TO A PEASANT

Before Baal Shem got his name for being a real saint and healer, and moved to Mezhbizh, he had lived with his wife, Sarah, in a little settlement of Troscianec, where they had run an inn. However, Baal Shem was no businessman and it was Sarah who struggled to make both ends meet. Her husband's task was to take the cows to the pasture and tend to them, but even this was not a job for him. He would let the cattle graze while he sat in the shade of a tree engrossed in the study of holy books.

Every day at dawn, before going to the pasture or commencing his daily activities, in the summer, as well as in the winter, Besht would go to perform his ablutions in the cool water of the nearby pond, which was situated in the field of a Gentile, Stefan Hajseniuk, the head of the village community.

Once, on a frosty winter morning, when the peasant was going to his ice-covered pond to draw some water from the air-hole he noticed bloody footprints on the snow. Intrigued and alarmed, he followed them and found out that the blood-stained track led directly to the inn. Next morning Hajseniuk hid in the bushes to see who would be walking that way. To his great amazement he saw Besht, whose bare feet froze to the snow while he was staggering towards the pond. Each time he tore them away from the glaciated ground, blood stains remained on the snow, like casually dropped roses. The peasant felt so sorry for the poor Jew that from then on he would go out every night and put some straw on Besht's way. Once, however, he started out a bit late and came across him near the pond. Baal Shem thanked the peasant for his kindness and good heart, and invited him to the inn, where he treated him to some vodka. He also told the man to come to him for help if he ever found himself in difficulties.

And it really happened so several years later. Besht was already famous as a wonder-rabbi and dwelt in Mezhbizh, in Podolia. Hajseniuk fell into considerable problems in the village of Troscianec as a large sum of money was missing from the community funds. Although the head of the village swore by all the saints that he was not to blame, the peasants turned a deaf ear to Hajseniuk's pleas and even threatened to slay him. Seeing that matters were going from bad to worse, the wronged man left the village furtively, under the cover of darkness, and headed towards Mezhbizh. His rather exhausting wanderings took many nights and days and when finally, after many hardships, he reached his destination another obstacle emerged before him. In no way could Hajseniuk contact Besht, as the Saint, was continuously surrounded by innumerable crowds of sick people who sought healing, unhappy people who expected consolation and the pious Chasidim who hungered for Besht's divine teaching and good counsel. He spent several weeks waiting for his turn, but without any luck. In the end he thought of approaching the synagogue beadle and sending a word of message to Besht through him.

As soon as the Rabbi had learnt of Hajseniuk's presence he had the peasant brought into his house. The man explained the nature of his worries and begged Baal Shem for help. The Saint listened to his words with deep sympathy and gave him a choice of three things. The peasant could choose between a long life, big wealth and the position of the community head in Troscianec, which he would hold for the rest of his days. Hajseniuk, however, could by no means make up his mind and at last, after long deliberation, shifting his weight from one foot to the other and scratching his head, he stammered out: "Oh, dear Rabbi, I'd like to have all those three things! " The peasant's practicality and simplemindedness made Besht smile. He then promised Hajseniuk to fulfill his three wishes.

The man thanked his benefactor warmly and set out on the way back to his native village. When he was going along the roads, paths and byways most unusual things happened to him. Everyone he met on the way gave him some gift or a coin. Thus, by the time he came to Troscianec he had accumulated quite a handsome fortune. A bigger surprise yet awaited him in the village. All the peasants came out joyfully to bid him welcome. As the successor to his post had turned out to be a crook and drunkard, they begged Hajseniuk to forgive them and to accept his former position again.

In this way Baal Shem's promise came true. Hajseniuk built himself a new house, in which he dwelt with his family in happiness. The rumour has it that he lived to be a hundred, enjoying the health of a young man, and that he was the head of the village till his very last days.

THE SEER OF LUBLIN

The Seer of Lublin was the nickname given to Tzaddik Jacob Isaac Horovitz of Lublin already during his lifetime, as he was known for his supernatural ability to read people's past and future, as well as seeing the current events taking place in very distant locations, such as for instance the court of the Emperor of Austria.

Jacob Isaac was born in 1745 in Yuzefov, where he spent his childhood and early youth and remained there till the day of his wedding, to which he was forced by his family. Convinced that this marriage was not part of God's plan for him, Horovitz left his native place and started his wanderings from the court of one famous tzaddik to another. He spent his time there studying the Kabbalah and listening to the teachings of the tzaddikim. The most famous of his spiritual masters was Rabbi Elimelekh of Lezhensk (1717-1787), to whom the discovery of the power of Jacob Isaac's eyes is ascribed.

Before Jacob Isaac settled in Lublin for good he had been a rabbi in Rozvadov and Lancut and it was there that crowds of people started gathering around him. They were Chasidim seeking the divine knowledge as well as the sick and the unhappy who hoped for the alleviation of their sufferings.

Rabbi Horovitz became famous as one of the chief leaders of the Chasidic movement in Poland. One of the interesting facts about him is his interpretation of history, based on looking for some divine signs which would announce the nearness of the Messianic Era. The Tzaddik saw them in the Napoleonic wars and he respected the Great Corsican to such an extent that he appealed for general support for him. The call, addressed to all Jews, but primarily to the Chasidic leaders, did not, however, bring any response. In the Seer's opinion such a unanimous approval would have hastened the fulfillment of the Biblical promise and ensured the quick end of the Diaspora, as well as the meeting of all the Jews in Jerusalem.

Jacob Isaac Horovitz died in 1815 from the injuries sustained after he had fallen out of the window of his house. The date of his death coincides with the Ninth Day of Av, when Jews mourn the destruction of the First and Second Temple in Jerusalem.

HOW JACOB ISAAC HOROWITZ CAME TO BE KNOWN AS THE SEER OF LUBLIN

According to a Chasidic legend Jacob Isaac Horowitz had had to roam many a road before he finally settled in Lublin and acquired the fame of a wonder-rabbi.

Already in his native Yuzefov he was regarded as an infant prodigy, since he never had to be forced to prayers and studying. Instead of seeking the company of other boys of his age, to play with them and make pranks, he would spend all his days in the synagogue bent over the Holy Scriptures. As a youth he became even more pious, and devoted his time to studying the Torah and the Talmud to such an extent that he hardly ever slept. Eventually a day came when he packed several books and a bit of bread and set out on a quest for learning and wisdom.

Whenever he had to go through a forest the words of prayer and psalms were on his lips all the time, so no wonder that the devil and other evil forces inhabiting the backwoods were after him. The sound of holy words and the sight of such piety was unbearable for them, so they intended to bring about his peril and silence him forever. The Tempter employed all his well tested methods to achieve his goal and seduce Jacob. Once he materialized before the Saint in the shape of a fiery-eyed wolf, hoping that Jacob would be scared and cast a curse or would at least forget his prayers for a moment. Another time he incarnated himself into the body of a pretty woman who was to show Jacob Isaac the ways of sin. But with such a pious man as he was none of those devilish tricks would work. Apparently the only available

---

means left at the devil's disposal was killing the Saint, so in order to accomplish this the Evil One started throwing mighty boulders and uprooted trees at him. But here too did the Fiend make a mistake in his clever calculations, as the power of Jacob's pious invocations was such that the devilish missiles could do him no harm.

After many weeks of wanderings the youth came to the court of the famous Maggid of Mezritsh. His stay there, however, was not a long one, because in a short time a divine voice in his dream ordered him to continue on his way. Thus, whenever Jacob wanted to spend more time at one of the renowned tzaddikim's places the very same voice would command him to leave. The youth became quite weary of these eternal wanderings in the wilderness, so when he reached the town of Lancut he decided to remain there for good and set up his own court. Soon enough a large number of supporters gathered around him, as the advice he gave to people would always turn out accurate. More than once would they also sense that the Tzaddik was capable of reading their souls and that the past and the future had no secrets from him.

But by God's decree Jacob was not supposed to stay in Lancut for too long, either. After some time he again heard the familiar divine command in his dream, urging him to leave. This time it directed him to Lublin. Even in his immense wisdom Jacob could by no means make out that order, as at that time there resided in Lublin a Rabbi Ezriel who was such an ardent opponent of the Chasidism that he was generally known by the nickname of the "Iron Head." For this reason no miracle-working tzaddik could even dream of moving to Lublin. Nevertheless the divine command was repeated night after night, so in the end he decided not to postpone the journey any longer and set out as he had done so many times before. Finally he arrived in Vieniava, a shabby suburb of Lublin, where many a poor Jew lived. Among them Jacob Isaac decided to settle.

Hardly had he done so when crowds of people again started gathering around him, as they had already heard of his divine faculties and good advice. No wonder, therefore, that Rabbi Ezriel was soon well informed about the situation and boiling with anger. Out of envy he tried to forbid people to say anything good about Jacob Isaac. It did not amount to much, however, and the crowds of people in need who teemed in Vieniava grew bigger from day to day.

One morning a real miracle took place there. It so happened that a man from the city of Lublin came to Vieniava to visit a relative of his. He was walking along the narrow, muddy street and watching the beadle run from house to house and knock three times on every door to wake the people up for morning prayers. He had just knocked on Jacob Isaac's door and was about to continue on his daily round when suddenly the door thrust open and who should appear in it but the Tzaddik himself. With a motion of his hand he stopped the beadle in his progress and for a moment went back into the house. When he reappeared on the threshold he was holding a basin and a pitcher with water. Without a word he showed them to the beadle, who fell down to his knees before the saintly man and loudly implored God's and Jacob Isaac's forgiveness.

The man of Lublin who had witnessed the event, later questioned the beadle about the whole thing. The latter explained he had left his house in the morning in such a hurry that he had forgotten to perform the obligatory ablutions. Because of his divine sense the Tzaddik knew about the beadle's sin, so he gave him some water to enable him to atone for it. The fame about that event spread in the neighbourhood with the quickness of lightning and in due time it also reached Lublin.

It gained Jacob Isaac so many new supporters that without any further obstacles he could move in to the city. Since that time people started calling him the Seer of Lublin.

THE DEATH OF THE SEER OF LUBLIN

For a number of years the saintly Jacob Isaac was a Rabbi in Lublin, where he won a reputation for his great wisdom and was known as a real miracle-worker. From near and afar the people who sought his counsel came and so did the crowds of disciples who wanted to catch a glimpse of the Saint's face at least. Thus, his court was always teeming with people, in particular on various holidays, when the Tzaddik's powers seemed to grow even stronger. It also happened many times that the very sight of the Saint transformed the hearts of sinners and unbelievers, inducing them to prayer and winning their souls for the Almighty.

No wonder that the Evil One, who never ceased to observe the Seer's doings, did not have a quiet minute and was always beating his brains out trying to get rid of his pious adversary. What's more, he knew that if the Seer lived a bit longer and continued mending people's ways, he would thus speed up the coming of the Messiah. Satan had pondered over this for so long that finally he discovered a way to put his plan into practice. Since he had no direct access to the Tzaddik, who was surrounded by many pious Chasidim, he was determined to silence their prayers at least for a moment. In order to accomplish this, however, he had to cloud their minds. He went about carrying out his infernal plot on the very day of Simchat Torah, and decided to use wine for this purpose.

As usual, on such a solemn occasion, many a Chasid arrived at the Tzaddik's court in Lublin. They celabrated the day with joy, singing, dancing and drinking freely, the intoxication making their spirits even higher. The ecstatic singing went on continuously and the dance became so passionate that it bore resemblance to a kind of trance. The Tzaddik was looking at the revellers with his eyes, from which nothing on the earth or in the upper spheres could be hidden, and suddenly he saw the devil's plot behind this joy.

A momentary chill overwhelmed him and a mighty shudder shook his body at that sure sign of approaching death. Only the mutual prayer of all the present Chasidim could save his life. Thus he called to them, but his voice seemed to be hovering in some vaccum, unheard by anyone. He repeated his desperate call several times, but the song, dance and drink had such an effect on the people, as if their souls were transported into an entirely different world. Thus Jacob Isaac summoned his wife, Beikele, and asked her to follow him to the loft and watch him there while he was immersed in prayers. He warned her to fight sleepiness by all means and under no circumstances to leave the room. Only such help could now upset the devil's plan.

Many hours did they spend in their pious watch and despite the feeling of immense tiredness Beikele managed not to sleep a wink. Aware of the fact that his plot might yet be ruined, the devil thought out a new trick and instantly a knock at the door could be heard in the room. The Tzaddik's wife had sprung up from her chair and was about to open and see who was coming, when she suddenly remembered her husband's warning. She resumed her seat and no longer paid any attention to the knocking, even though it was growing louder and impatient. Finally there was silence.

In the meantime, the Evil One was fiercely grinding his teeth and looking for another solution. Soon a new device was ready. This time it was addressed to the tender heart of the woman. And so, all of a sudden, Beikele heard the desperate crying of a baby, coming from behind the door. After awhile that heart-breaking whining changed into plaintive sobbing. Mindless of all the warnings, without so much as casting a glance at her husband, Beikele ran into the corridor to help the miserable baby. Hardly had she crossed the threshold when the crying stopped as if cut with a knife. There was not a living soul in the darkness looming over the stairs.

Beikele stood horrified, having realized in the nick of time, that it had all been Satan's dodge. She hastily went back to the room, but the Tzaddik was no longer there. His mysterious disappearance must have been the devil's doing as there was no other door leading to the room and the window was closed.

At the same time two young Chasidim walking along the street were passing the Seer's house. They heard some groans coming from the nearby bushes. At first they were quite scared, thinking that the Evil One was trying to lead them astray, but after a moment they gathered enough courage to check what was going on. A sorry sight presented itself to their eyes, as in the bushes they found the Tzaddik with bones broken, bruises and other injuries all over his body. Without any delay they cautiously carried him home, where the distraught Beikele took proper care of him.

Nothing, however, could restore Jacob Isaac's health. The illness confined him to bed and his terrible pangs of suffering lasted for a very long time. Then the saddest day came, the Ninth Day of Av, the month of mourning. The light of the Seer's life expired, leaving crowds of bereaved Chasidim filled with pain and unassuaged sorrow.

CHELM

A caricature of a Jew (by L. Ostrowski)

*T*here is a considerable problem involved in the discovery of the origin of the phenomenon connected with the ascription to the Jewish Chelm the status of a town of fools. Perhaps it results from some event whose actual memory has been lost somewhere in the meanders of the distant past. Chelm humour parallels the analogous phenomena in the folk tradition of many countries. Thus, for instance, the English have their fools of Gotham and German people laugh at the inhabitants of Schilda. Very frequently these comic characters are also ironically referred to as Wise Men.

In the Jewish tales we can trace numerous attempts to define the sources of the naive, laughter-inducing foolishness of the Chelmites. One of the explanations connects it to an event in times as remote as the creation of the world. According to this God sent one of His angels to the Earth with two sacks, one full of wise souls, the other of stupid ones. The winged emissary was to distribute them all over the world in even proportions. Unfortunately he had a mishap when he was flying over Chelm. The sack with the stupid souls was torn by a protruding rock and its whole content fell on that spot.

A different story has it that the Jews of Chelm had to carry water to the town from a nearby river the path to which led down the steep slope of a hill. The way back, with buckets full of water, was definitely not an easy one, hence the jokes originated ridiculing the "imprudence" of the Jews who carried empty buckets downhill and full ones uphill. A retrospective search for similar paradoxes was supposed to be projected on everything that went on in Chelm.

The most realistic version, however, is presented by Sol Liptzin in "A History of Yiddish Literature." He links Chelm's anecdotal foolishness to the 15th-century figure of Reb Yossifel, a leader of the town's community. Although a learned man, he was so detached from reality and displayed such naivety that he would believe virtually anything he was told. And when it came to decision-making, in connection with different conflicts and issues concerning the town, he always wanted to reconcile the parties at odds so much that he invented the most ingenuous solutions which not only complicated the matters further, but also led to funny situations.

Whatever the explanation is, the funny tales about Chelm are still a vivid and timeless element of Jewish humour and tradition. They can be found in many anthologies, in anonymous versions typical of folk literature, as well as in a transformed, literary form in the fiction of well-known Jewish writers, like Isaac Bashevis Singer for instance.

THE FOOLS OF CHELM, CLEVER IDEAS AND THE MOON IN A BARREL

The town of Chelm was continuously in poverty, so its inhabitants never stopped racking their brains how to find a remedy to this situation and begin a rich life. The biggest contribution to these ponderings was, of course, made by the town Elders. These aged citizens distinguished themselves considerably from the remaining Chelmites. They not only had longer beards, pointing to the fact that they had lived in this world for a long time, but above all the level of their stupidity was much higher. In fact it was infinite and that's why the Elders considered themselves the biggest sages of all time, whose wisdom surpassed even King Solomon's.

Except for the Sabbath, the eminent men would meet daily in the seat of the kahal to ponder together, from early morning till late evening, over the problem of Chelm's poverty. Newer and newer ideas entered their heads and each of them was more stupid that the previous one. The Elders, however, regarded them as such a brilliant and exquisite creation of their thought that it would really be a pity to put them into effect. Their practical fulfillment could simply be less ingenious than the original products of the sages' minds. A law was therefore hastily passed that all the ideas should be written down in a special chronicle kept for this purpose. This is what was done and as the creative faculties of the Elders were inexhaustible, the size of the chronicle soon amounted to one hundred thick volumes. As to Chelm's poverty it throve and fared quite well. Entering every household in town, it made the people so miserable that they started to claim

A caricature of a Jewess (by L. Ostrowski)

that one of the wonderful ideas be sacrificed so as to deliver Chelm from its straits.

Thus the order of the day at the kahal was disturbed by constant quarrels, since the decision as to which idea should be chosen was a difficult one. It seemed the bickering would last forever, but all of a sudden another bright idea occurred to one of the respectable Elders. He suggested they ought to send out letters to all the Jewish communities in Poland and offer them the ideas registered in the chronicle for sale. Assuming that they would get even as few as seven gold coins for each idea, though in reality they were worth much more and some were indeed invaluable, Chelm would gather enough gold to erect several gold mountains in the town. This, on the other hand, would make many strangers come to Chelm to see this unusual sight, and they would have to pay for this divine pleasure, of course. In this way the town would really become a rich and prosperous city, the capital of the world in fact.

Everyone liked the idea so much that the local scribe immediately started putting it into effect. For a whole long year, day and night, he was busy writing and he used up tonnes of paper. And what ideas there were! Real pearls! Better than pearls! Priceless diamonds! What wonderful inventions the Chelmites offered to the ignorant world! People could, for instance, get richer by studying the frogs' language and then teaching it to the children of the rich. They could also go into business and sell on commission jars and bottles in which the breath of Chelm's sages was enclosed. A person who bought one such vessel and breathed in the air from it would become almost as brainy as they. There was also a proposal to call the street dust gold and then anyone could have plenty of this noble metal. Such and even cleverer ideas were amassed in large quantities in Chelm, but one of them was by far the cleverest one. It must have really been invented by the genius of all time. No wonder it was priced at one hundred gold coins, though this was still much beneath its real value. No one had any doubt as to that and, in fact, the whole community hoped that the purchaser would, out of his own accord, pay them at least one thousand coins. Ay, what a clever idea it was! In order to become wealthy one should do no more no less, but take the moon down from the sky. Kept in a coffer, it would guarantee a comfortable life to many a family for hundreds of years, as it was common knowledge that the moon was made of silver and that it kept growing out all the time.

The letters with the ideas had been sealed, sent out to villages, towns and large cities and the Chelmites began their impatient wait for the gold to come pouring to Chelm. They waited one, two, three months but not a single piece of gold turned up. Soon it became quite clear to everyone that they had been cheated and that the people who would now exploit Chelm's brilliant ideas, were by no means willing to pay for them. Great lamentation broke out in Chelm and the Elders assembled for an extraordinary council to decide how to handle the situation. This time they did not even have to embark on lengthy debates, as already at the opening moment the oldest sage suggested a solution. He pointed out that the moon was still visible in the sky, which meant that no one had so far taken it down. Why? But, of course, thanks to the Chelmites' exceptional wisdom and foresight! When putting the idea on sale they did not reveal the way it was to be implemented. Under these circumstances it became more than obvious that the town of Chelm was to employ its own device quickly, before anyone else could take advantage of it.

Here, however, a small but disturbing problem arose, as it soon turned out that the Elders had so far not invented a way to take the moon down. But what kind of problem was that for such eminent sages? After a moment of intensive thinking the solution was reached and already the same night all the inhabitants of Chelm gathered in the town's market, in the middle of which a huge half-filled barrel of water was placed. The moonrise was anxiously awaited and as soon as the shiny dial appeared in the dark sky the barrel was moved in such a way that the precious heavenly body was fully reflected in the water. The rejoicing Chelmites, having captured the moon with so little effort, covered the barrel with a heavy lid and rolled it to the kahal building.

In the morning, almost as early as dawn, all the Chelmites started swarming there in wait for the Elders who were to divide the moon-silver justly among the community. How big everyone's amazement was, when on opening the barrel it turned out there was only water inside. Among the general bedlam and lamentation the people started wondering about the reason for the vanishing of the moon. The answer was simple, of course, so even the youngest sage could explain the facts. Somebody who had dishonestly come into possession of the idea invented in Chelm did not know how to capture the moon, therefore he had waited for the Chelmites to accomplish it. The previous night he must have mixed with the crowd in the market and later followed the Chelmites, to see the place where the moon was hidden. Then, after everyone had gone to bed, he stole Chelm's treasure, which had been so painstakingly obtained. Since it had evidently happened in the middle of the night the impudent thief must have already been far away from Chelm, so a resolution was passed not to undertake a pursuit.

And where did all of Chelm's bad luck come from? First the Chelmites were cheated, then robbed. Well, I'll tell you. It is because of their poverty, for everybody knows that life is tough on the poor. Thus the Elders reached a conclusion that next time they would capture the sun and accumulate a lot of gold in this way. In order to do that, however, they had to get rich first. Otherwise if they again embarked on this venture as paupers, malicious fate would bring them another failure.

CHELM IN DEEP TROUBLE

Problems in Chelm were nothing new under the sun, for they had existed as long as the town itself. One generation of fools passed away and another generation came, but Chelm went on forever. Almost every day its inhabitants would find themselves some new problems. Fortunately, however, they had their world-famous Council of Elders, which, always in session, solved the emerging matters to the general happiness of all the Chelmites.

The story of one of the problems faced by the community happened to spread all over the world. The difficulties came into being when a thief built himself a house on the outskirts of the town and settled there for good. After having served his prison sentence of several years in Lublin's jail, the fellow was set free, to his own content and to the utmost dismay of the honest people. The town of Chelm was panic-stricken and although its inhabitants were not in possession of much wealth they would stay in their homes day after day, without going out even for a moment. Watching their shabby belongings engrossed them so much that the Rabbi fell into despair at seeing the synagogue empty all the time. He knew that only the Elders could be of help, so he went to them, although, not being a native of Chelm, personally he did not think too highly of the town sages.

He found them all in the kahal building, completely lost in thought. As he soon learnt, the alarming news had already reached the sages, as a result of which all their mental faculties were engaged in the attempt of freeing the town of its difficulties. It was generally known that the traditional methods by which the burglar operated were door-prizing and window-breaking. It was therefore heatedly debated how to invent such protection which would keep him from employing either of his tricks. Normal locks and padlocks were a mere trifle to open and any child, not even necessarily blessed with Chelm's wisdom, could accomplish that much.

After several days of lengthy discussions and intensive thinking the problem became even more urgent, as the Chelmites, who had been staying in their homes all the time, started suffering from scarcity of food. As the supplies in their pantries had been used up it was even feared that all the Chelmites would soon die of starvation and the world would be deprived of their great wisdom. If such were the case, it would also result in the fact that there would be no one to watch the property, which would, in turn, fall prey to the thief.

In this situation the Elders made one more common and impressive mental effort, announcing the decree to all the concerned. Thereupon all the doors and windows in Chelm were to be walled up and the houses were to be entered through the chimneys, to which ladders were to be fixed to make the climbing easier. The Chelmites, all happy, undertook the work gamely and within one day every window and door in the town was nicely bricked up.

However, contrary to the common hope, that was no end to the problem, as in several days' time it turned out that the Chelmites were unable to distinguish between day and night. Thus the Rabbi was still dissatisfied and the synagogue still empty. The Melamed also complained of growing difficulties in gathering the boys in cheder, as even he himself did not know when to go to the shtibl. Quite soon the feeling of dissatisfaction became a general phenomenon. Additionally it was noticed that for some obscure reason the walled-up doors and windows caused an increase of the amount of oil used for lamps. But a real

---

outcry was raised after the thief had got into one of the houses through the chimney.

The Elders had again to assemble for council. First of all they ordered all the chimneys pulled down so that such an audacious crime could not take place again. The problem of the walled-up doors and windows, however, remained unsolved for a time. It became obvious that they should be unwalled but no one knew what to do next. After several more days of frenetic debates and busy mental activities a perfect solution was reached. And how simple it was! The only thing to do was to break all the windows in town and it was more than certain that the burglar himself would not be able to break them. As to the doors, could anything have been simpler? The Chelmites were to unhinge them and carry them on their backs wherever they went. Even if the thief had been born in Chelm and his wisdom were greater than the wits of all the Elders put together, he could not invent a means to prize a single door open.

The joy which seized the whole town seemed almost endless. Only a couple of grumblers expressed their doubts, saying that from carrying the doors all the Chelmites would soon become hunchbacks. The Elders were about to consider this plaint as well, but before they had time to do that the problem had solved itself. One day, quite unexpectedly, the thief entered all the houses and robbed them of everything there was to be robbed. How he had managed to do that without breaking the windows and prizing the doors remained an inscrutable mystery for everyone in Chelm. But at least they got rid of the unwelcome citizen, who in fear of punishment, vanished into thin air with his loot.

The doors were therefore replaced and apparently everything went back to normal. The resigned Elders, as well as the inhabitants of Chelm reached the conclusion that the thief must have been aided by some unearthly power, from which the honest people could not protect themselves in any way.

GOLEM

*T*he word "golem" has a Hebrew origin and means a shapeless mass or a formless lump, however in the contemporary mind it rather evokes associations with the old legend of a Prague Rabbi, Judah Loew (1525-1609), who is believed to have created a clay man, or golem, with the help of his Kabbalistic knowledge and magic.

Similar abilities, testifying to the attainment and penetration into the biggest world mysteries, are also attributed to many other famous rabbis and tzaddikim. Among them are mentioned such figures as Elijah, nicknamed the Gaon of Vilna, or Elijah Baal Shem of Chelm. The legend included in this collection tells the story of the latter. Also Besht was supposed to possess a golem who used to help him with the everyday household chores.

If we present the act of the golem's creation in its simplest form, without going into the details of the secret formulas, it is reduced to putting life into a colossus made of clay. The life-giving element was a tetragrammaton, a clay tablet or a piece of parchment with the Hebrew word "emet," meaning truth, inscribed on it. It was attached to the golem's forehead, put under his tongue or suspended on his neck. The last of these methods was mentioned in the first written sources pertaining to this subject. The powerful word could also be directly inscribed on the golem's forehead. The whole creation act was based on a belief in the holiness of the characters of the Hebrew alphabet as well as in their divine potential.

In most of the tales and legends, however, the golems brought trouble to their makers, as being devoid of mental faculties they could not engage any reasoning in the performance of the tasks assigned to them. It also happened that their immense strength was marked with some monstrous qualities, so instead of protecting people they became a threat to them and even to the whole world. Thus it became imperative to annihilate them, which was carried out by removing the tetragrammaton.

Creation of a Golem

RABBI ELIJAH OF CHELM
AND A GOLEM

The town of Chelm, though most frequently associated with with its fools, was once famous as an important centre of Jewish learning and it was there that Rabbi Elijah, an eminent sage and master of the Kabbalah, lived in the 16th century. He seemed to be in possession of all the mysteries of the earth and heavens, and people maintained that whenever he fell into his mystic thoughts his soul separated itself from his body and soared to the Seventh Heaven to enter communion with God's Presence. And each time the wise man turned his eyes to earthly matters he always noticed the unhappy and the sick, whom he healed with the power of his prayer. Thus after some time people started calling him a Baal Shem.

Rabbi Elijah's great piety and other virtues were known in many countries, yet it was quite a different thing that won him admiration all over the world. One year the community of Chelm realized that their Rabbi, instead of staying in his study, spent whole nights and days locked up in the attic. At the beginning people thought that the elderly man was seeking shelter from the burning sun, as the summer was really very hot that year. This also seemed to explain the fact that the Rabbi would take his Kabbalistic books with him. What took the entire community aback and made them wonder was only the story told by the beadle who acted as a helper to the Rabbi. Though he was generally known as a talebearer his account of the matters caused a lot of commotion and fear in the town.

Well, the beadle spread a rumour (ay, may God spare him the fires of Gehenna for this sin!) that Rabbi Elijah had taken to conjuring some tricks in the attic. For this purpose he had ordered the beadle to carry there several bucketfuls of clay and a troughful of water. What he did with the clay and water afterwards, however, the beadle did not know, although he was trying (ay, how boundless God's patience is!) to peep in through the keyhole. Unfortunately, the Rabbi, being aware of his curiousity, had taken the precaution to putty up not only the keyhole but also all the slits in the door. Then he locked himself in the attic and did not go out for many hours.

When he eventually left that unusual place of seclusion, quite a crowd of people gathered around his house was awaiting him. The mob was attracted by the feeling of growing curiousity. Everybody hoped for an exciting event or at least for some variety amidst the everyday dull reality. They not only were not mistaken, but what they saw considerably surpassed all their expectations. Rabbi Elijah coming downstairs was followed by a mighty figure, which resembled a man in shape, but nevertheless was certainly not of human flesh and blood. The body of the giant, which could hardly go through the door, was the colour of dried clay and the features of his face, thick and inexpressive, seemed to denote a person not capable of any mental effort.

The crowd was awestricken. Many a curious inhabitant of Chelm took to his heels at this sight, but in some people curiousity proved stronger than fear. These drew back a little, awaiting the further developments from a safe distance. Seeing the crowd, the Rabbi pointed at his unusual companion and explained that his name was Golem, as the word meant a formless mass. By means of the word "emet", meaning truth, inscribed on a piece of parchment and attached to the colossus' forehead, the Rabbi had put life into it. However, as it was a creation of man's not God's hand, the giant lacked the gifts of reason and speech and was thus able only to carry out the orders of his maker. Since he was, however, endowed with extraordinary physical strength, both the Rabbi and the community hoped that the Golem would help them with various chores.

The great admiration for the Rabbi's divine power filled all the people and it was additionally accompanied by the hope that with the Golem's help the life of Chelm's community would become much easier and safer. They saw in him a live Biblical hero, a powerful protector from pogroms and the enemies of Israel. Rabbi Elijah, on the other hand, appeared to be equal to the Creator.

Not before long, however, the inhabitants of Chelm, as well as their Rabbi, were in for a bitter disappointment. It was true the Golem did not lack in strength and there was no weight he could not lift, but his brainlessness was such that instead of being a helper he became much of a nuisance. Although he set about carrying out the Rabbi's orders willingly, he did not engage thinking in his work, which was therefore bound to cause trouble.

One day, when leaving for the synagogue, the Rabbi told the Golem to fetch home some water. The latter presently started busying himself between the kitchen and the well in the yard. He had no idea, however, what to do with the water, so he poured one bucketful after another onto the floor. The Rabbi spent several hours in the synagogue, so when he came back home the furniture was floating all over the house like a fleet of ships on the sea waves.

Another time, on a Friday morning, the Golem was ordered to chop some wood so he went to the nearby forest with an axe in his hand. When it was already getting dusky and the clay dumbhead had not returned yet, the Rabbi started to worry. He remembered the flooded house from some time before and realized that his awkward helper would not stop chopping out of his own accord. There was also a danger that he would profane the approaching Sabbath. Thus the Rabbi had the beadle put the horses to the wagon and they rode post-haste to the forest to fetch the Golem. On reaching their destination they saw huge stakes of cut-down trees and the once impressive Chelm forest had been reduced in size to a mere grove.

When finally Rabbi Elijah brought the Golem back to town the sun was already past sunset and for the first time in his saintly life he was almost late for synagogue. Later at night, before retiring to bed, the Rabbi said his prayers asking God to enlighten him in a dream what to do with the Golem. In the morning when he woke up he knew the answer. He waited till the evening and when the last hymns bidding farewell to the departing Sabbath were over he gave the Golem a cup of wine spiced with sleep-inducing herbs. Soon the giant was fast asleep and the house shook with his mighty snoring. The Rabbi, who had waited just for this moment, tiptoed to him and delicately removed from his forehead the life-giving parchment with the word "emet". Instantly, near the stove, a heap of clay appeared in place of the Golem.

And such was the end of the Golem of Chelm. In later years many rabbis, in different parts of the world, tried to repeat Rabbi Elijah's accomplishment, but they did not have much luck with their creations, either. The brainless clay giants always brought misfortunes on their masters, since a real miracle of creation can only be performed by God.

BIBLIOGRAPHY

— Bałaban, Majer. *Przewodnik po żydowskich zabytkach Krakowa*. Kraków: Stowarzyszenie „Solidarność -B'nei B'rith", 1935, (reprint).

— Bałaban, Majer. *Żydowskie miasto w Lublinie*. Lublin: Wydawnictwo Fis, 1991.

— Duda, Eugeniusz. *Old Jewish Cemetery and Remuh Synagogue — Short Guide*, Transl. Ewa Basiura, Kraków: Argona-Jarden Art.

— Howe, Irving & Greenberg Eliezer (ed.). *A Treasury of Yiddish Stories*. New York: Penguin Books, 1990.

— Liptzin, Sol. *A History of Yiddish Literature*. New York: Jonathan David Publishers, 1988.

— Patai, Raphael. *Gates to the Old City*. Detroit: Wayne State UP, 1981.

— Safrin, Horacy. *Przy szabasowych świecach*. Łódź: Wydawnictwo Łódzkie, 1986.

— Samsonowicz, Henryk (ed.). *Polska Jana Długosza*. Warszawa: PWN, 1984.

— Shmeruk, Chone. *The Esterke Story in Yiddish and Polish Literature*. Jerusalem: The Zalman Shazar Center, 1985.

— Trachtenberg, Joshua. *Jewish Magic and Superstition: A Study in Folk Religion*. New York: Atheneum, 1974.

— Unterman, Alan. *Dictionary of Jewish Lore and Legend*. London: Thames and Hudson, 1991.

Drukarnia
Uniwersytetu Jagiellońskiego
31-110 Kraków, ul. Czapskich 4
tel./fax (012) 422-59-41
e-mail: drukarnia@adm.uj.edu.pl
www.uj.edu.pl